Little
RAINDROP

AUTUMN
PUBLISHING

Written by Melanie Joyce
Illustrated by Gina Maldonado
Designed by Lee Italiano
Edited by Emily Bruce

An imprint of Igloo Books Group,
part of Bonnier Books UK
bonnierbooks.co.uk

Published in 2019
by Igloo Books Ltd, Cottage Farm
Sywell, NN6 0BJ

Manufactured in China. 1219 001
10 9 8 7 6 5 4 3 2 1

Library of Congress Cataloging-in-Publication
Data is available upon request.

ISBN 978-1-83852-397-8
IglooBooks.com
bonnierbooks.co.uk

Little RAiNDROP

AUTUMN
PUBLISHING

When I was a raindrop,
I lived up in a cloud.

One day, Thunder rumbled by
and BOOMED out very loud.

"Come now,
little raindrops,
get ready to let go.
You've got important
work to do down in
the world below."

A **FLASH** of zigzag lightning **streaked** across the sky.

"Oooh!" cried all the raindrops.
"See you later, Cloud. Goodbye!"

They jumped into the air, and I jumped with them too.

"Have fun," said Cloud. "I wish that I could come along with you!"

Down and down we fell, giggling, shouting, "Wheee!"

Oh, what fun to be a raindrop flying free.

From high up in the sky, we saw the earth below.

Sunbeams shone through us and made a lovely big rainbow.

After that,
quite suddenly,
I landed with a

And dribbled down the tail

I saw a friendly mole,
who was digging by some shoots.

SHLUP!

Before I knew it, I'd been
sucked into their roots.

I traveled slowly up the stem. It was quite a climb!

"Hello," smiled the flower bud. "You're here just in time."

"This way," the flower told me, and then it opened wide.
What a nice surprise to see my raindrop friends inside!

We had so much fun, sharing stories of our day,
as the warm sun slowly set, and the light faded away.

We tried to count the stars, instead of counting sheep,
but the petals were so comfy that
we all fell fast asleep.

When the morning came, the sun shone **hot** and **bright**.

We all felt quite peculiar, sort of shaky and light.

Slowly we drifted upward,
there was no way to resist.

For I and all my raindrop friends
had turned into a mist.

"What's happening?" I asked,
floating higher with the crowd.

The others laughed and said,
"We're going back into our cloud!"

"**Welcome back,**" said Cloud.

"I hope you all had fun. It's time for you to rest, now that there's lots of sun."

"But soon the wind will blow again,
and turn the weather vane.

And you'll have more adventures,
next time it starts to . . .

...rain!"

When it rains,
water droplets fall from
the clouds down to the earth.
There, they trickle into rivers or seep
into soil, where they are sucked up into
the roots of thirsty plants. When the sun
shines, the water droplets warm up and turn
into mist, which floats up to the sky.
As the droplets cool down again,
they turn back into clouds.
Now the water cycle
can begin again.